MAZECRAFT

3-D MAZE GAMES AND COOL PUZZLES

ARCTURUS

Packaged for Arcturus by Infinite Jest Ltd
Text: Katherine Sully
Illustration: Peter Lawson
Design: Jessica Moon
Maze Design: Simon Ward
Project Management: Gill Shepherd

Editor for Arcturus: Joe Harris
Cover Illustration: Adam Clay

Picture credits: Shutterstock Bomshtein 45 br, Cristobal Garciaferro 47br

ISBN: 978-1-78599-735-8
CH004905NT
Supplier 26, Date 0516, Print run 5329

Manufactured in China

2 4 6 8 10 9 7 5 3 1

HOW TO USE THIS BOOK

Hi there! I'm Ace McDanger, world-famous treasure hunter, and I'm looking for an intrepid assistant. Are you brave enough to act as my guide?

THE CREATURES IN EACH MAZE BLOCK THE ROUTE.

SHOW ME A SAFE PATH TO THE TREASURE CHEST.

KNIGHT TIME

Look out for the sword-wielding knights as you storm this castle. And beware of the spikes! The catapult can hurl you into the treasure chamber.

Collect all four gold coins along the way and tick them off.

Find the catapult to get to the chest.

64 65

LOOK OUT FOR THE TERRIBLE TRAPS!

THE INSTRUCTIONS EXPLAIN HOW SPECIAL ITEMS CAN HELP.

GATHER ALL THE GOLD COINS OR JEWELS.

JUNGLE HIJINX
Beware of snakes and spikes as you explore this jungle ruin! Find the key that unlocks the gate to the treasure chest.

Collect all four gold coins along the way and check them off.
Find some fish to lure away the crocodile!

NASTY NINJAS

Hi-yah! Can you find the shadow that belongs to this dangerous ninja?

M[illegible]S M[illegible]ZE

These Martians don't look friendly! Steer clear of the creatures and avoid falling down any craters. Can you reach the treasure?

Collect all four precious jewels along the way and check them off.

POLAR PERIL
Find a path around the stalagmites and hungry polar bears to fetch your ice pick. You'll need it to dig out the chest.

Collect all four gold coins along the way and check them off.
Find an ice pick to hack through the ice blocks!

LlE I V slu

Don't let the aliens spot you! Find the lever to switch off the force field around the treasure.

Collect all four precious jewels along the way and check them off.

MARS LANDING

Can you land safely on Mars? Find and circle twelve words connected with the Red Planet.

V	G	E	Y	S	E	R	G
O	R	O	C	K	E	T	R
L	A	L	R	L	A	V	A
C	P	L	A	N	E	T	V
A	I	S	T	O	R	M	I
N	E	R	E	D	U	S	T
O	N	O	R	B	I	T	Y
M	A	R	T	I	A	N	S

1. PLANET
2. LAVA
3. GEYSER
4. RED
5. MARTIAN
6. VOLCANO
7. ORBIT
8. ROCKET
9. DUST
10. STORM
11. CRATER
12. GRAVITY

The leftover letters will spell another space word. What is it?

_ _ _ _ _ _

DINO DANGER

How will you make it past the dinosaur guarding the treasure? Try feeding it a giant piece of meat! But beware of the hot lava pools...

Collect all four gold coins along the way and check them off.
Find a tasty piece of meat to feed the T Rex!

WOLF TRAILS

Which path should Ace follow? One trail leads straight to the treasure, but the other two lead to hungry wolves!

TOMB OF DOOM

Ace has discovered an ancient tomb. Find a passage that avoids the ninjas and flames to reach the hidden chest.

Collect all four precious jewels along the way and check them off.

ON SAFARI

Sneak past the lions lurking in the long grass and find a way to cross the crocodile-infested river to reach the treasure.

Find a boat
to cross
Crocodile River!
Collect all
four gold coins
along the way and
check them off.

DEADLY DIVE

Steer clear of stinging tentacles and prickly pink coral as you dive down to search for the lost treasure.

Collect all four precious jewels along the way and check them off.

ALIEN INVASION

Every alien has a clone... except for one. Can you match the pairs to discover which one is the odd one out?

GOBLIN GROTTO

Don't let the grotty goblins grab all the treasure. They've hidden it behind rubble, so you'll need a pick to dig it out. But beware of sneaky spikes and mantraps!

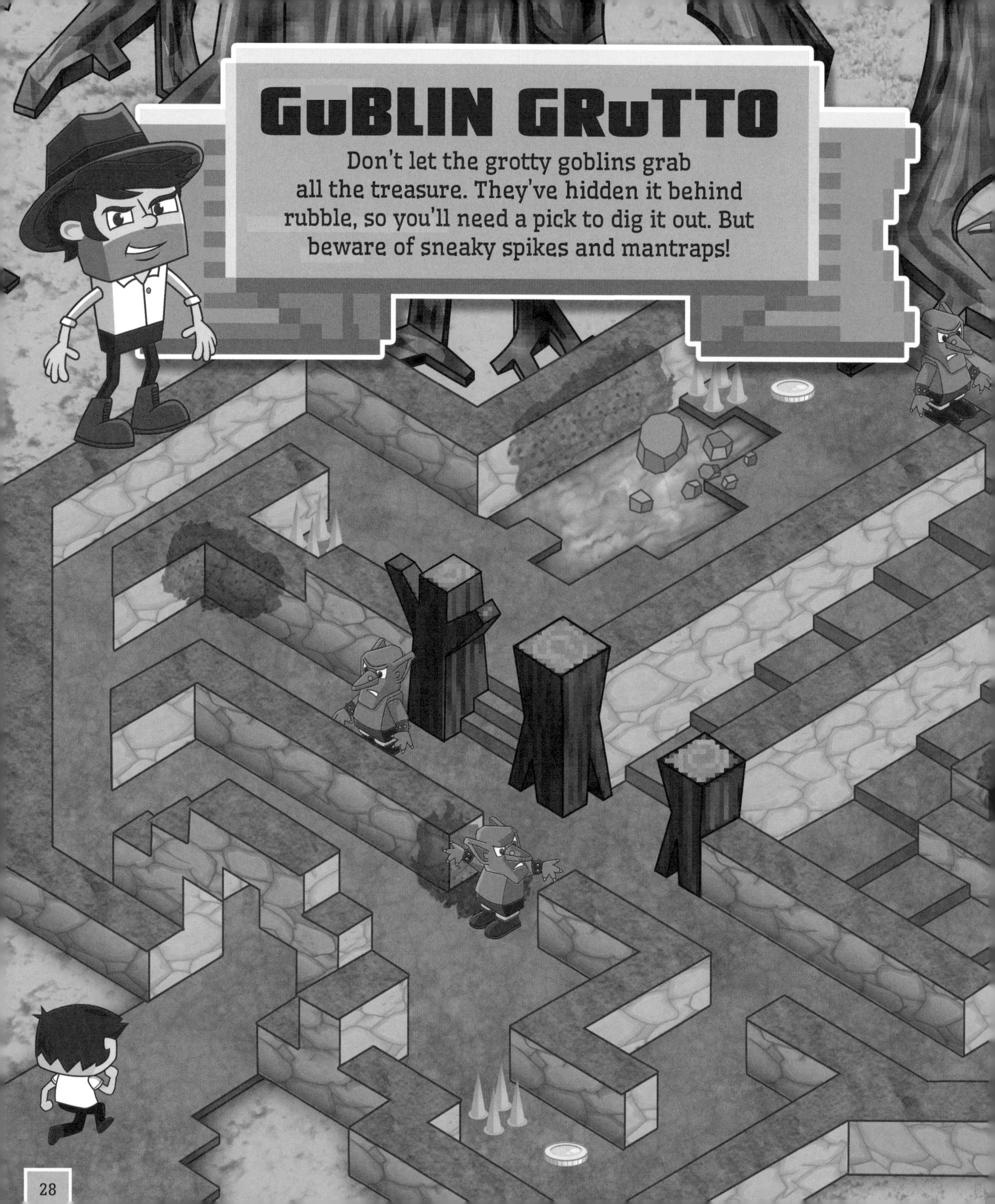

Find a pick to dig out the treasure chest!
Collect all four gold coins along the way and check them off.

Ace is fishing in an ice hole.
Which line— A, B, or C — leads to the fish?

Greedy Weeds

Hack your way through this overgrown maze to discover a hidden treasure chest. Avoid the hungry, man-eating jungle plants!

Collect all four precious jewels along the way and check them off.

MOLTEN MAZE
The lizard people are watching you! Find a water bucket to put out the fires and reach the treasure before they catch you.

Collect all four gold coins along the way and check them off.
Find the water bucket to put out the fire.

ZOMBIE ZONE

You'll need to be brave to get past these horrible zombies and fires. The treasure is hidden in the basement.

Collect all four precious jewels along the way and check them off.

BIRD BRAIN

Are you seeing double? Find the matching pairs among the birds. Which two birds do NOT have a matching pair?

FUTURE SHOCK
Ace is exploring a distant future populated by deadly robots. Can you find your way to "Teleport 1?" It will transport you to "Teleport 2"... and on to the treasure chest.
TELE
PORT
2

Use teleports 1 and 2 to reach the treasure.
Collect all four gold coins along the way and check them off.
TELE PORT
1

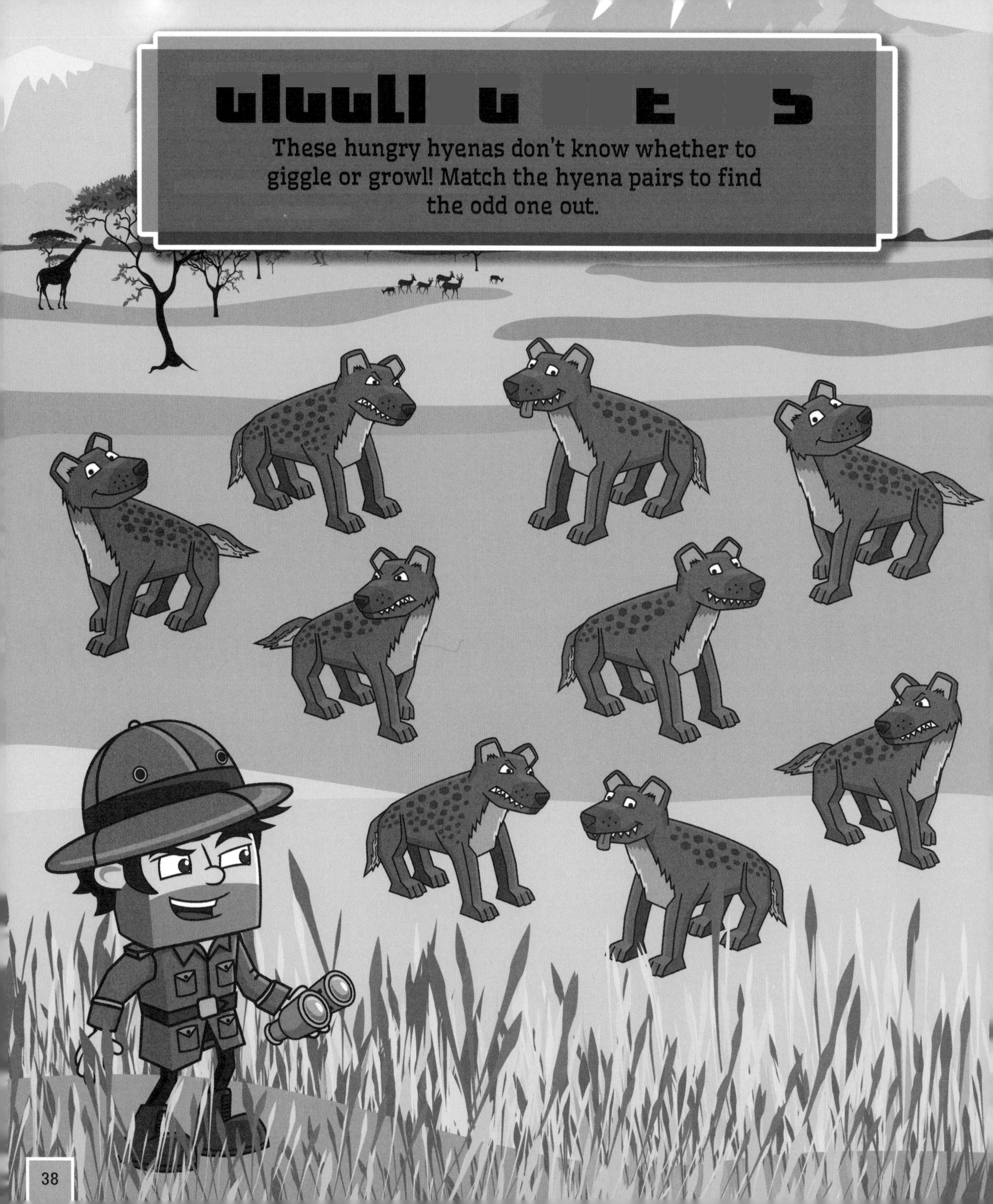

These hungry hyenas don't know whether to giggle or growl! Match the hyena pairs to find the odd one out.

BLACK LAGOON
Beware of the monsters in the Black Lagoon! They will try to grab you on your way to find the treasure chest.
Collect all four precious jewels along the way and check them off.

LABYRINTH
You have stumbled upon a lost labyrinth. Find a secret passage to the forgotten treasure. Beware of minotaurs and spikes!
SECRET PASSAGE

Collect all four gold coins along the way and check them off.
EXIT
Find the secret passage to the treasure.
SECRET PASSAGE

MET A YETI?
Your quest is to free the treasure from the frozen ice. But watch out for the yetis!
Collect all four precious jewels along the way and check them off.

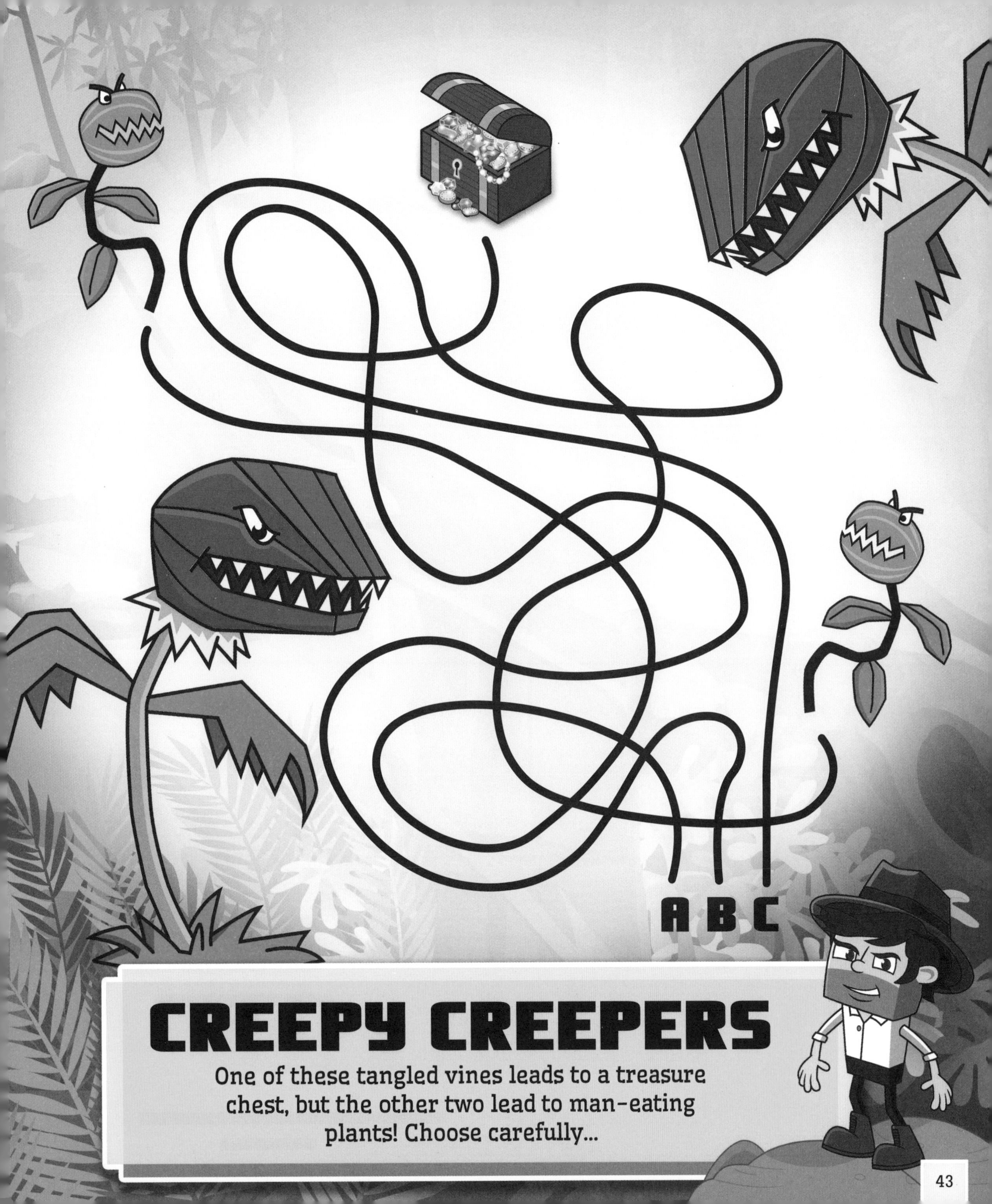

CREEPY CREEPERS

One of these tangled vines leads to a treasure chest, but the other two lead to man-eating plants! Choose carefully...

MER-KINGDOM
Take a deep breath as you enter the watery kingdom of the merpeople. You will need a key to open the gates.
Collect all four gold coins along the way and check them off.

Find the
key to unlock
the gates.

ZOMBIE PAIRS

These three zombies have lost their shadows. Match the zombies to their shadows so they can be reunited again.

TAIL STING
Beware of stinging scorpions and prickly cacti as you cross the desert to claim the chest.
Collect all four precious jewels along the way and check them off.

TIGER TIGER!
This jungle is as dangerous as they come. Look out for piranha-infested water and ferocious tigers! Find a saw to cut up the tree blocking the way to the treasure.

Find the saw to cut up the fallen tree.
Collect all four gold coins along the way and check them off.

FAIRY FOREST

This forest is filled with magic and spells. If you bump into a pixie, fairy, or goblin, they will send you back to the start!

Collect all four precious jewels along the way and check them off.

FU FIS

Can you find ten orange and white striped clown fish hiding on the reef?

CASTLE DRACULA
This creepy castle is crawling with monsters. Find some garlic to scare away Dracula, so you can reach the chest. Beware of trapdoors!

Collect all four gold coins along the way and check them off.
Find the garlic to get rid of Dracula.

[illegible] TIME

A volcanic blast has transported you back to the time of the dinosaurs! Find and circle the twelve hidden words in the grid below.

N	P	V	O	L	C	A	N	O
E	R	R	E	P	T	I	L	E
S	E	M	A	M	M	A	L	S
T	H	E	X	T	I	N	C	T
D	I	N	O	S	A	U	R	I
S	T	O	B	I	R	D	R	F
E	G	G	I	L	A	V	A	E
C	O	N	I	F	E	R	C	R
E	S	W	A	M	P	R	A	N

1. DINOSAUR
2. SWAMP
3. LAVA
4. VOLCANO
5. NEST
6. EGG
7. REPTILE
8. MAMMALS
9. BIRD
10. CONIFER
11. FERN
12. EXTINCT

The leftover letters spell a secret phrase. What it it?

_ _ _ _ _ _ _ _ _ _ _

_ _ _

IPPO SW M

Tread carefully through the swamp, avoiding the mantraps and hippos. There's treasure to be found!

Collect all four precious jewels along the way and check them off.

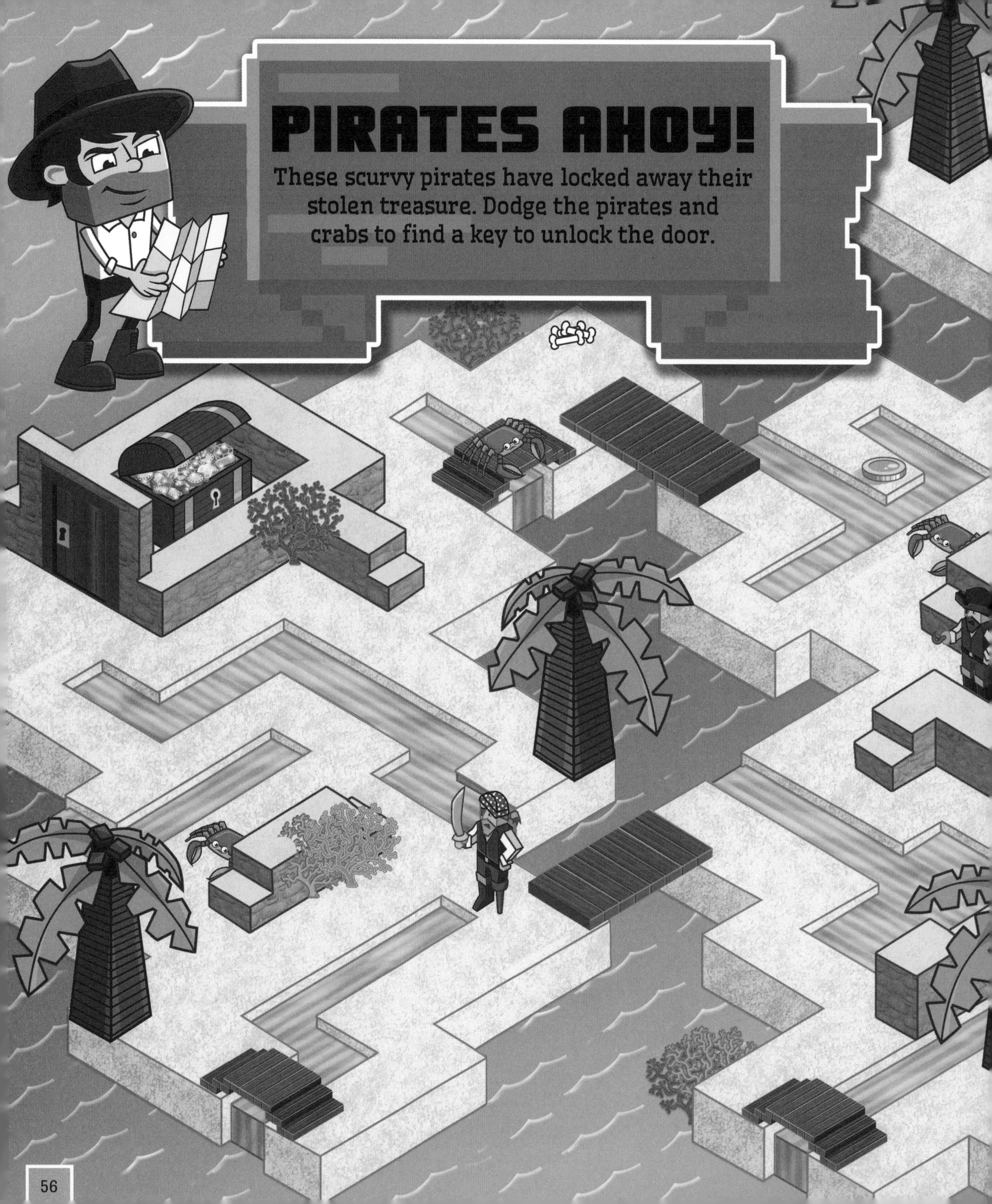

PIRATES AHOY!
These scurvy pirates have locked away their stolen treasure. Dodge the pirates and crabs to find a key to unlock the door.

Collect all four gold coins along the way and check them off.
Find the key to open the door.

ERUPTION!
Find the treasure before the volcano erupts!
Beware of dinosaurs living deep
below the surface.
Collect all
four precious jewels
along the way and
check them off.

RAT-DOKU

Are you smart enough to outwit the rats? Each row, column, and mini-grid in this sneaky sudoku puzzle should contain the numbers 1 to 9.

	1		2	7	8		3	
	4		3		1		9	
2								6
		8	6		3	5		
3								4
		6	7		9	1		
9								1
	8		9		2		6	
	2		4	3	6		5	

ICE AGE
Woolly mammoth and prehistoric tigers prowl the ice. Find an ice pick to dig out the treasure. Beware of sharp ice spikes!

Collect all four gold coins along the way and check them off.
Find the ice pick to dig out the chest.

SHARK REEF

Find and circle the shark names below. The leftover letters will spell out some friendlier sea animals.

H	A	M	M	E	R	H	E	A	D
D	S	A	N	D	T	I	G	E	R
O	C	A	R	I	B	B	E	A	N
N	L	P	R	E	Q	U	I	E	M
U	Z	W	H	I	T	E	T	I	P
R	E	C	A	T	S	H	A	R	K
S	B	S	A	W	S	H	A	R	K
E	R	B	L	A	C	K	T	I	P
H	A	I	N	C	A	R	P	E	T
W	O	B	B	E	G	O	N	G	S

1. BLACKTIP
2. CATSHARK
3. WHITETIP
4. SANDTIGER
5. CARPET
6. REQUIEM
7. HAMMERHEAD
8. CARIBBEAN
9. WOBBEGONG
10. NURSE
11. SAWSHARK
12. ZEBRA

What word do the leftover letters spell out? Write it in the space below.

__ __ __ __ __ __ __ __

Space aliens have invaded the moon base!
Sneak past them to reach the treasure,
but don't step on a bomb!
Collect all four precious jewels along the way and check them off.

KNIGHT TIME
Look out for the sword-wielding knights as you storm this castle. And beware of the spikes! The catapult can hurl you into the treasure chamber.

Collect all four gold coins along the way and check them off.
Find the catapult to get to the chest.

DINO PARK

Somewhere in this prehistoric park is hidden a treasure chest. Can you reach it before feeding time?

Collect all four precious jewels along the way and check them off.

ICE PUZZLE

Can you follow the right path to rescue the frozen penguin? Be careful... the other paths lead to hungry polar bears!

RIVER CROSSING

Can you brave the fearsome jaguars and alligators to reach the boats? It's the only way to get to the treasure chest!

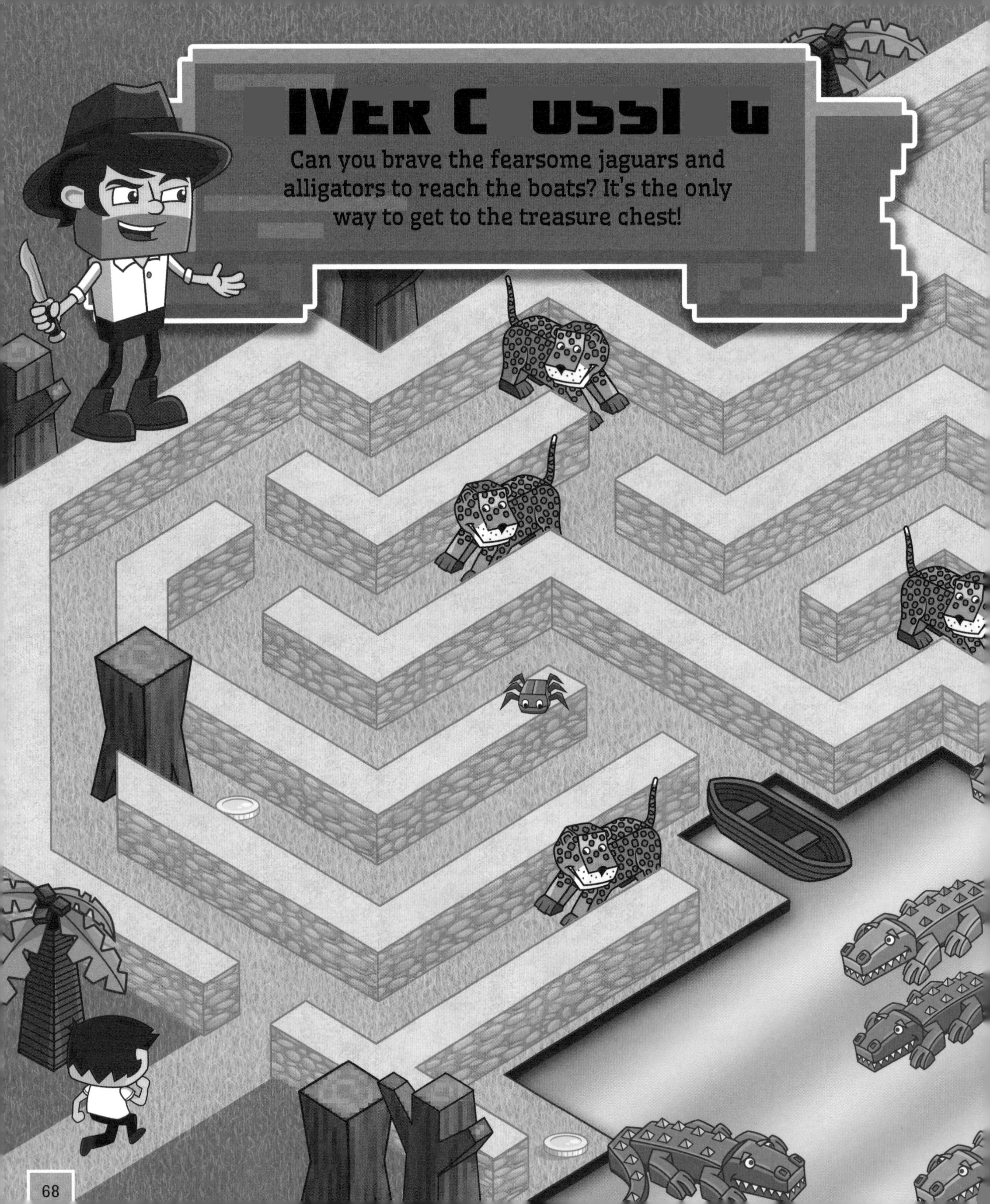

Collect all four gold coins along the way and check them off.
Find the boats to cross the river.

LITTLE BIGFEET

These woodland creatures may have big feet, but they're not very tall! Match the pairs to find the odd one out.

SHARK ATTACK
Are you getting a sinking feeling? This deep-sea treasure is guarded by sharks and prickly coral.
Collect all four precious jewels along the way and check them off.

STONE AGE
The paintings in this cave warn of prehistoric perils. Look out for fires and angry cavepeople. You'll need a pick to break up the boulders!
Find the pick to reach the treasure.

Collect all
four gold coins
along the way and
check them off.

WILD WOOD
You've spotted more treasure in the wild wood. Can you get past the Bigfeet, piranhas, and traps to reach it?
Collect all four precious jewels along the way and check them off.

VIKI G S IELDS
These Vikings are looking for a shield containing numbers that add up to 21. Can you spot it for them?
9 4 6 4
1 9 5 5
9 2 9 3
7 6 4 5
11 0 4 8
6 3 3 7
4 4 6 7

Beware the dragon's lair! Only a magic ring can lure away the big, red dragon guarding the treasure. Look out for trapdoors!
Find the ring to dazzle the red dragon.

Collect all
four gold coins
along the way and
check them off.

Two alien spacecraft have landed on this comet.
Can you spot five differences between them?

Massive mousetraps have been set all over this house. Avoid the rats and traps to get to the treasure.

Collect all four precious jewels along the way and check them off.

Super-Ace has snuck into the secret H.Q. of his arch-enemy, Ivan Eville-Plan. Dodge the robots to find the lever and deactivate the lasers around the treasure.

Collect all four gold coins along the way and check them off.
Find the lever to shut down the lasers.

VILE VIKINGS

The Vikings are coming! Save the treasure before they plunder the island. Look out for traps!

Collect all four precious jewels along the way and check them off.

DOT-TO-DINO

Connect the dots to reveal what sort of prehistoric creature is hidden here.

MUMMY TOMB
Beware the curse of the mummy's tomb!
Find the secret tunnel to reach the treasure.
Watch out for mummies and spiders!
EXIT
Find the secret tunnel to the chest.
ENTRANCE

ENTRANCE
Collect all four gold coins along the way and check them off.

Do you have the knowledge to survive in a scorpion-infested desert? Find and cross out the words below. They could be arranged across, up, down, backward, or diagonally.

L	S	A	N	D	D	U	N	E
E	I	O	S	L	E	M	A	C
D	S	C	O	R	P	I	O	N
R	A	I	O	E	K	Y	O	C
A	O	U	O	L	O	T	F	A
Z	E	R	U	T	L	U	V	C
I	O	M	E	E	R	K	A	T
L	R	S	N	E	A	O	K	U
H	A	W	K	B	E	S	T	S

1. CACTUS
2. SCORPION
3. BEETLE
4. LIZARD
5. CAMELS
6. VULTURE
7. TORTOISE
8. OASIS
9. HAWK
10. COYOTE
11. MEERKAT
12. SAND DUNE

The leftover letters spell some useful advice. What do they say?

_ _ _ _ _ _ _

_ _ _ _ _ _ _ _ _

ICE QUEEN
This chilly castle is home to ice monsters and polar bears. Find a safe route to the treasure and escape the Ice Queen!
Collect all four precious jewels along the way and check them off.

PUZZLE SOLUTIONS

Hi there, intrepid assistant! On the next few pages, you'll find solutions to all the different puzzles we encountered on our expedition. Each maze has red, green, and blue lines to show different achievements.

THE RED PATH LEADS TO THE SPECIAL ITEM NEEDED TO GET TO THE TREASURE CHEST.

THE BLUE PATH LEADS FROM THE SPECIAL ITEM TO THE TREASURE CHEST.

THE GREEN PATHS LEAD TO THE COINS OR JEWELS.

DID YOU AVOID THE TRAPS AND DANGERS?

page 4

page 6

Answer: Broken web, missing leg, stripy back, eyes, and longer teeth

page 7

page 8

page 10

page 11

Answer: Octopus

page 12

page 14

page 15

page 16

page 18

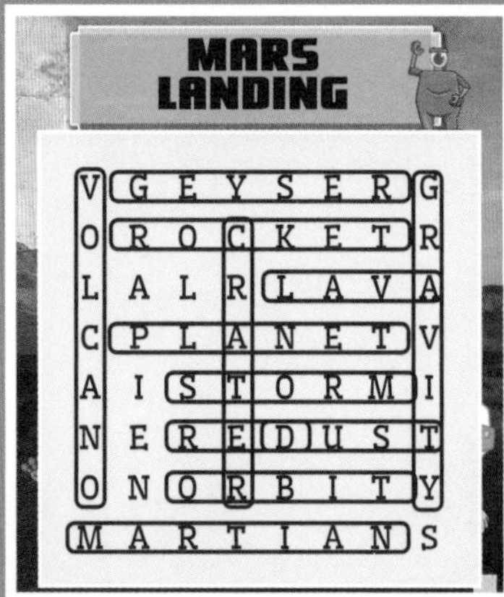

page 19
Answer: Aliens

page 20

page 22

page 23

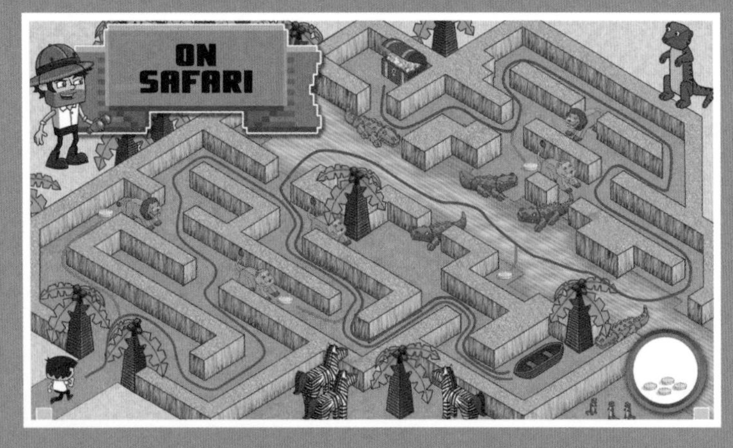

page 24

page 26

page 27

page 28

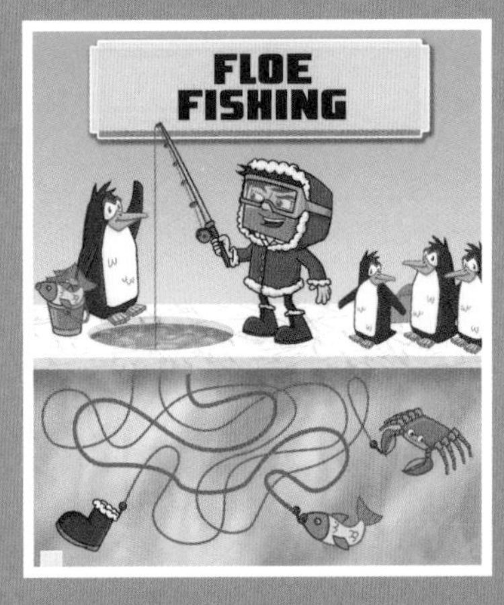

page 30

page 31

page 32

page 34

page 35

page 36

page 38

page 39

page 40

page 42

page 43
Answer: B

page 44

page 46

page 47

page 48

page 50

page 51

page 52

page 54

Answer:
Prehistoric Era

page 55

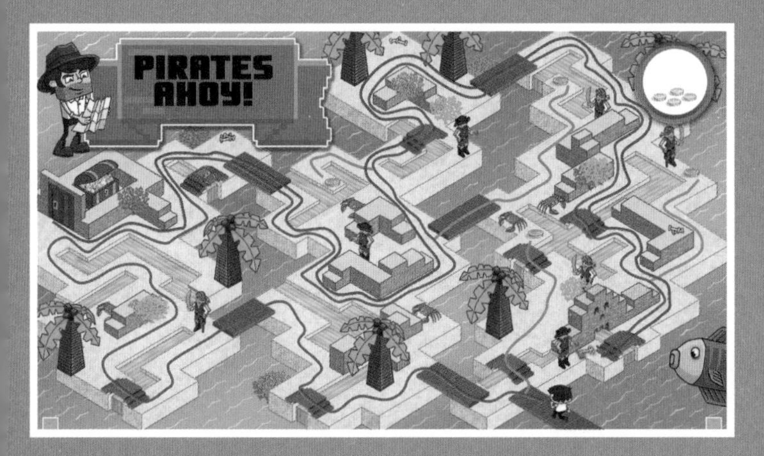

page 56

page 58

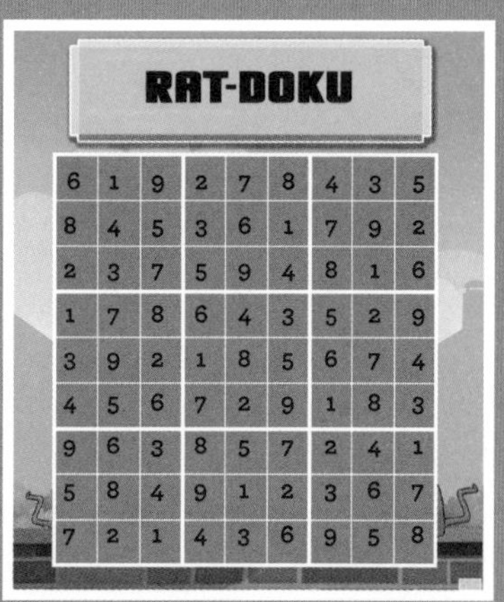

6	1	9	2	7	8	4	3	5
8	4	5	3	6	1	7	9	2
2	3	7	5	9	4	8	1	6
1	7	8	6	4	3	5	2	9
3	9	2	1	8	5	6	7	4
4	5	6	7	2	9	1	8	3
9	6	3	8	5	7	2	4	1
5	8	4	9	1	2	3	6	7
7	2	1	4	3	6	9	5	8

page 59

page 60

page 62

Answer: Dolphins

page 63

page 64

page 66

page 67

page 68

page 70

page 71

page 72

page 74

page 75

page 76

page 78

Answer: Laser, bolt, bolt, escape hatch, and foot

page 79

page 80

page 82

page 83

Answer: Diplodocus

page 84

page 86

Answer: Look out for snakes!

page 87

Did you spot these items on your MazeCraft adventure? Which pages were they on?